An A B C for

BABY PATRIOTS

By
Mrs Ernest Ames.

A, a.

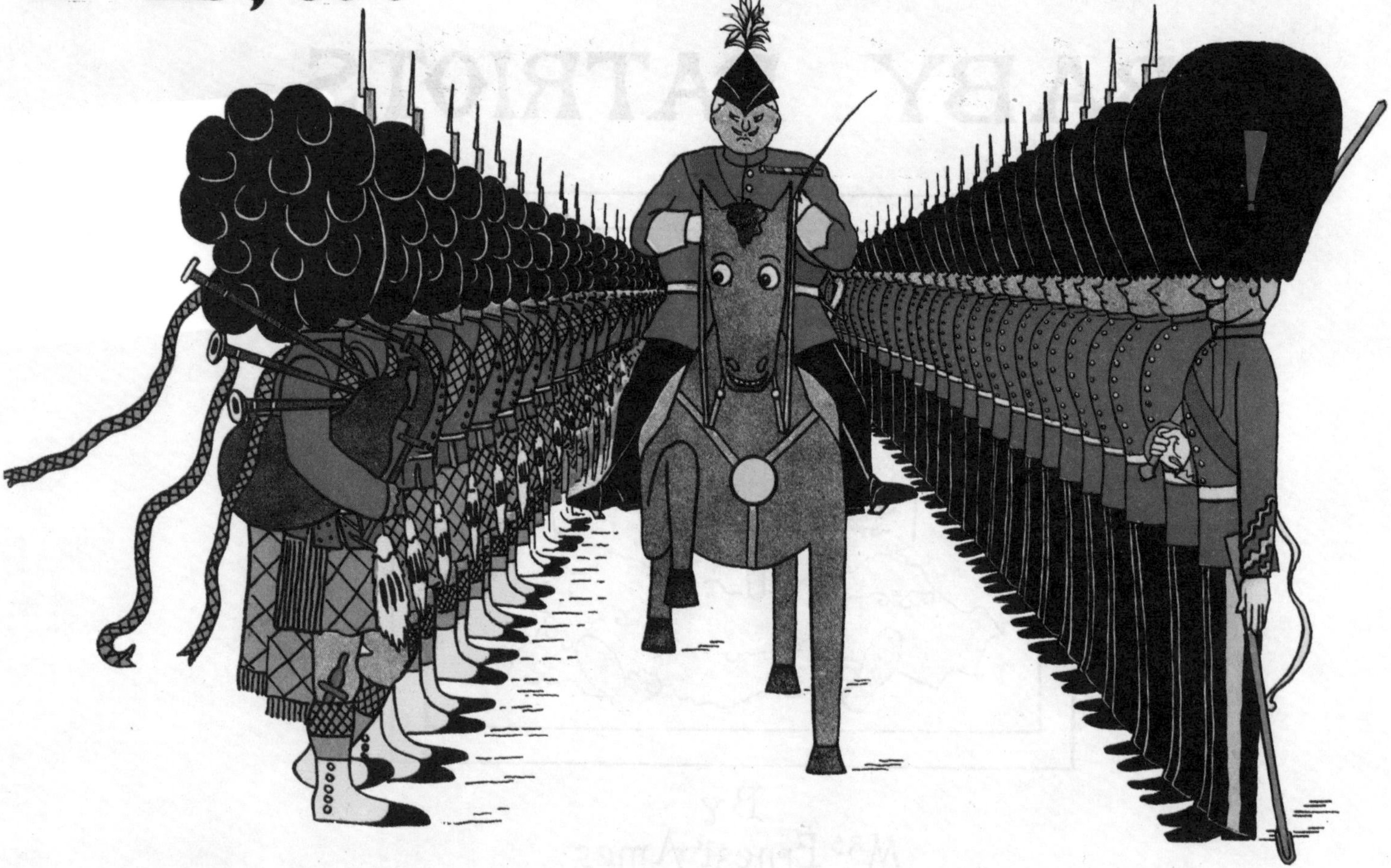

A is the Army
That dies for the Queen;
It's the very best Army
That ever was seen,

B, b.

PENINSULA
WATERLOO
CRIMEA
INDIA
CHINA
EGYPT
KHARTOUM

C, c.

B stands for Battles
    By which England's name
Has for ever been covered
    With glory and fame.

C is for Colonies.
    Rightly we boast,
That of all the great nations
    Great Britain has most.

D, d.

D is the Daring
We show on the Field
Which makes every enemy
Vanish or yield.

E is our Empire
Where sun never sets;
The larger we make it
The bigger it gets.

E,e.

F is the flag
    Which wherever you see
You know that beneath it
    You're happy and free.

F, f.

G, g.

G is the Game
We preserve with
such care
To shoot, as it
gracefully
Flies through
the air.

H is for Hunting,
  For this you've a box,
A thoro bred Hunter,
  Some hounds and a fox.

I is for India,
 Our land in the East
Where everyone goes
 To shoot tigers, and feast.

I, i.

J's for our Judges
Who sit in a row
And send folks to prison
When naughty you know!

J, j.

K is for Kings;
   Once warlike and haughty,
Great Britain subdued them
Because they'd been naughty.

K, k.

L, l.

L is the Lion
Who fights for the Crown
His smile when he's worried
Is changed to a frown.

M is for Magnates
So great and so good,
They sit on gold chairs
And eat Turtle
for food

M, m.

N is the Navy
We keep at Spithead,
It's a sight that makes foreigners
Wish they were dead.

O   is   the   Ocean
    Where   none   but   a   fool
    Would   ever   dare   question
    Our   title   to   rule.

P is our Parliament,
Commons and Peers,
They will talk if permitted
For months — nay for years.

P, p.

Q is our Queen!
It fills us with pride
To see the Queen's coach
When the Queen is inside!

Q, q.

R' s the Roast Beef
    That has made England great;
You see it here pictured
    Each piece on a plate.

S is for Scotland
    The home of the Scot!
It's wetter than England
    And isn't so hot.

R, r.

S, s.

T is the Tub
   That an Englishman takes
As a matter of course
   Just as soon as he wakes.

U is our Unicorn,
   Such a nice beast
His home is here now
   Though he comes from the East.

T, t.

U, u.

V's Volunteers
Who can shoot very straight;
They are drilled now and then
Between seven
and eight.

V, v.

W is the Word
Of an Englishman true;
When given,
it means
What he says,
he will do.

W, W.

X as a rule means
  The London Police
Who are paid by the Country
  For keeping the peace.

Y   is for youngsters
  Gilded and gay,
The newspapers call them
  The "Jeunesse dorée."

Y, y.

X, x.

Z is the Zeal
Which is everywhere seen
When a family practices
"God save the Queen."

Z, z.

First Published by Dean & Son in 1899. This edition © Old House Books, 2010 Moretonhampstead, Devon   www.OldHouseBooks.co.uk,   01647 440707